Clues to Meaning

Ann L. Staman

B

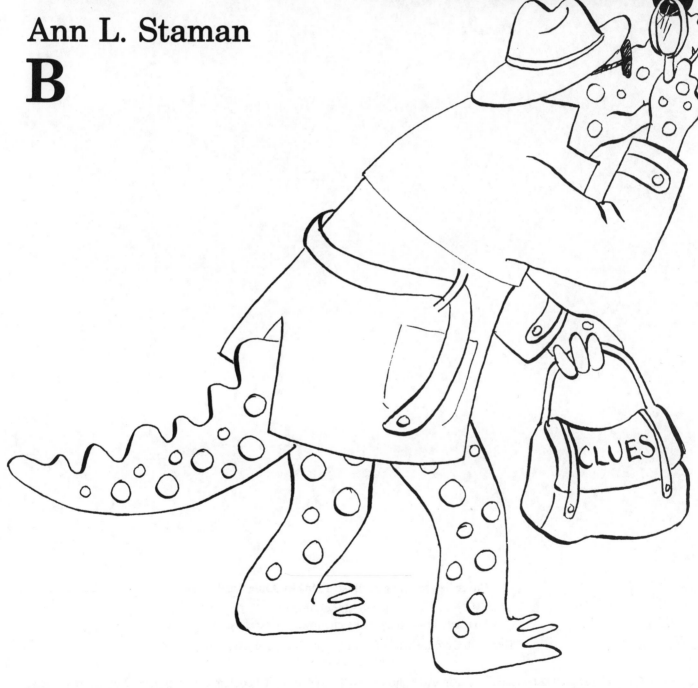

Educators Publishing Service,
Cambridge and Toronto

Cover design and text illustrations by Anne Lord

Dedicated to Mary Baltren,
who teaches first grade in Belchertown, Massachusetts.

Thanks to Dorothy Miller for all her patience, encouragement,
and editorial assistance.

Printed in the U.S.A.
ISBN 0-8388-2272-X

6 7 8 9 10 MLY 08 07 06 05 04

1

Now I am hunting for **short-a** clues.

Here are some . . .

Let's look for some more **ă** clues . . .

2

Write:

mat cat hat	
	c a t
	___ ___ ___
	___ ___ ___

man van pan	
	___ ___ ___
	___ ___ ___
	___ ___ ___

tag wag rag	
	___ ___ ___
	___ ___ ___
	___ ___ ___

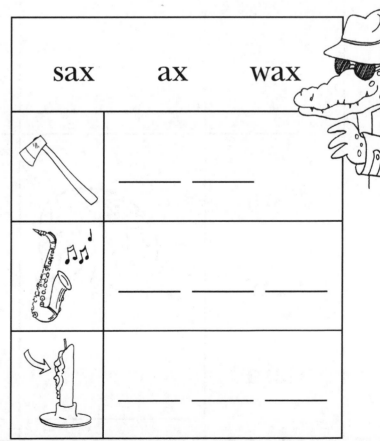

sax ax wax	
	___ ___ ___
	___ ___ ___
	___ ___ ___

Write:

add			
pad			
mad			
	p a d	_ _ _	_ _ _

nap			
lap			
cap			
	_ _ _	_ _ _	_ _ _

ham			
ram			
dam			
	_ _ _	_ _ _	_ _ _

4

Write:

	___ ___ ___	jazz
	___ ___ ___ ___	jam
	j a z z	Jack

	___ ___ ___ ___	pals
	___ ___ ___ ___	pack
	___ ___ ___ ___	pass

	___ ___ ___	Sal
	___ ___ ___ ___	sad
	___ ___ ___	sack

5

◯ and write:

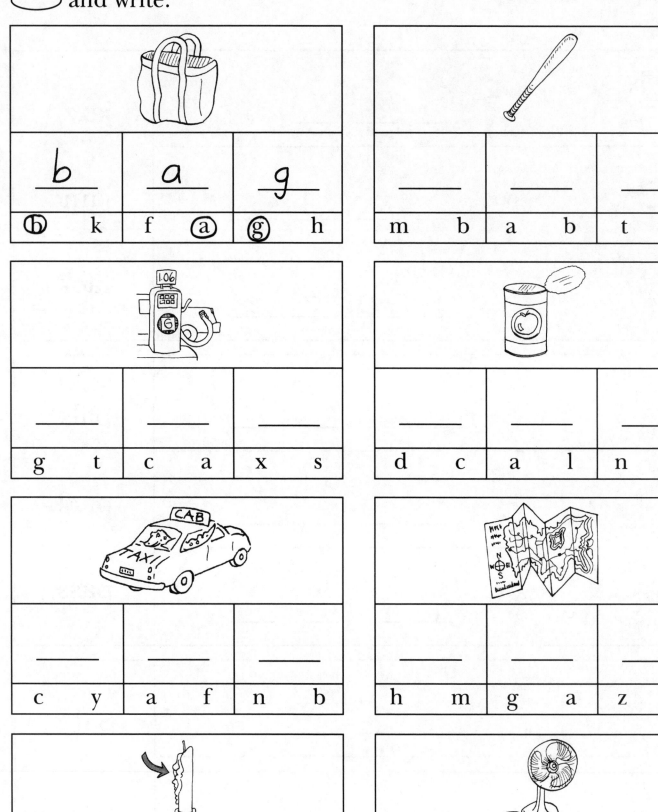

_b_	_a_	_g_
ⓑ k	f ⓐ	ⓖ h

m b	a b	t s

g t	c a	x s

d c	a l	n w

c y	a f	n b

h m	g a	z p

g w	a d	x i

f h	a p	n g

cap **(pack)** back pad	rat man ram ham	had add dam Dad
wag gas tag wax	tack cat back tag	dam mad Sam dad
fan mat tab bat	Pam Max tap map	sat wax sax cab
vat ran van nab	jab has jazz pat	sat mat sack sax
tack tan tax pan	jam pack sag jacks	sap pat pass bass

◯ and write:

dam				d a m
pals				_ _ _ _
tag				_ _ _
mad				_ _ _
cab				_ _ _
ran				_ _ _
ax				_ _

8

Match and write:

 VANS

ham

ADD

GAS

HATS

tac

Write:

Fill in the blanks:

bag	tack	can	pan
gas	cat	jacks	~~bat~~

Dan is up at ___ .   b a t

Santa has a ___ of toys.

Sal got a ___ of soup.

Ann is good at ___ .

Let's get a ___ for the eggs.

The van is out of ___ .

Sandy saw a black ___ .

Ack! I sat on a ___ .

Dad has this on his back. What is it?

It is a b __ __ __   __ __ __ __ __ .

11

Write:

cat

~~pad~~

fan

man

rat

Dad

Ann

ram

sat

bag

THINGS	
1	pad
2	
3	

PEOPLE	
1	
2	
3	

ANIMALS	
1	
2	
3	

X the one that does not belong:

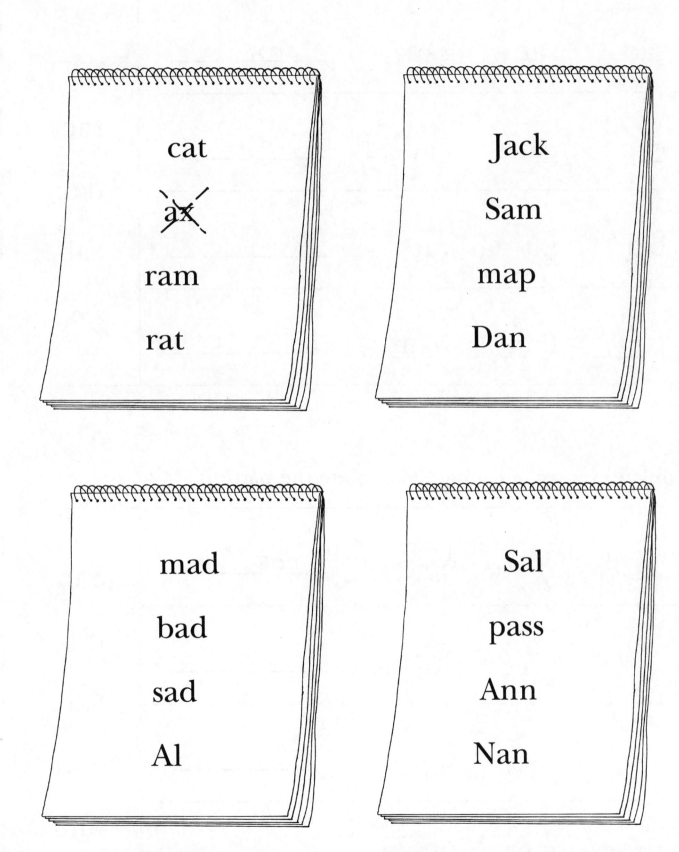

cat

~~ax~~

ram

rat

Jack

Sam

map

Dan

mad

bad

sad

Al

Sal

pass

Ann

Nan

Think about the **sounds**. Complete the pattern.

sad	sat	sap	sax	pat
cap	can	cat	_____	rack
bat	fat	rat	_____	dam
jam	Pam	ham	_____	cab
				~~sax~~

Think about the **meanings**. Complete the pattern.

			rat	Sam
			_____	~~rat~~
			_____	Sal
				had
			_____	van

14

Where do these belong?
* = bonus word!

~~pan~~	gas can
van	jam
ax	ham
* glass	* hammer

KITCHEN

1. _pan_

2. _____

3. _____

4. _____

GARAGE

1. _____

2. _____

3. _____

4. _____

Here is a page from a book I like.
Circle all the **short-a** words.

Then the (cat) ran fast, as fast as it
could—past the tree, past the
house, past the big pile of wood.

Look in a book **you** like.
Find a word with **short-a** in it. Put it
in a sentence. Then draw a picture
to go with your sentence.

Write:

Sam can play
the __sax__.

Ann can _____
in math.

_____ can
catch a dragon.

Dan   map   sax   bat   tap   add

Sal can _____
dance.

Matt can read
a _____ .

Nan can _____
the ball.

What can *you* do?

I can --

FOLD

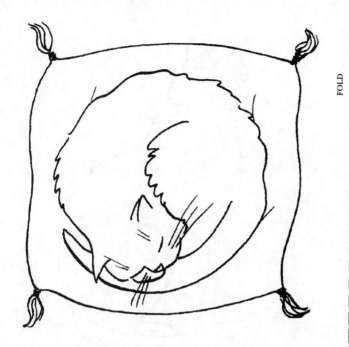

cats take naps.

8

CATS

Cats hiss.

1

FOLD

Cats chase rats.

6

Cats hunt.

3

19

Cats play.

2

After all that . . .

7

Cats purr.

4

Cats lap up milk

5

I get mad
when

Hi! I'm Isabel the Inchworm. I look for **short-i** clues.

Here are some . . .

in   ill

inch   igloo

Let's look for some more **i** words . . .

Write:

bit	sit	mitt		in	win	fin

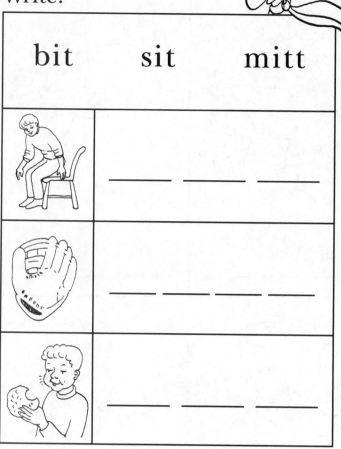

	____ ____ ____

	____ ____ ____ ____

	____ ____ ____

	____ ____

	____ ____ ____

	____ ____ ____

hill	pill	fill		zip	rip	lip

	____ ____ ____ ____

	____ ____ ____ ____

	____ ____ ____ ____

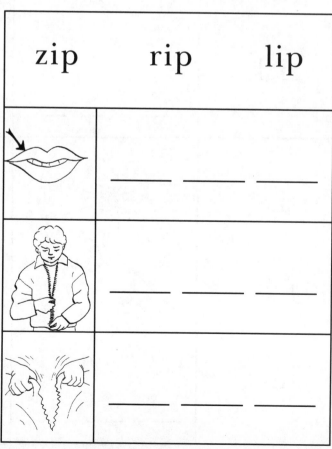

	____ ____ ____

	____ ____ ____

	____ ____ ____

23

Write:

pig wig dig			
kick lick sick			
six fix mix			

Write:

	— — —	**Liz**
	— — —	**lid**
	— — —	**lip**

	— — — —	**kids**
	— — —	**kiss**
	— — — —	**Kim**

	— — —	**bib**
	— — —	**Bill**
	— — — —	**big**

and write:

___	___	___
a z i	b p k	p k

___	___	___
p j d	i n r	

___	___	___
f l w	i d t	

___	___	___
d m i	s g e	

___	___	___
b c w	i n b	

___	___	___
s b i	v ck z	

___	___	___
l f g	i n p	

___	___	___
h r x	i t p	

hit hid him din	kick mitt Mick mill	gill pig bin big
gill hill lid dig	bit tip pit pig	wig win nip tin
lip hid hip pick	kick sick hiss kiss	fizz fin fib will
Tim mitt fit mill	wick miss six mix	kit Jim Kim him
rip rib bib bill	kill wick lick lit	ill fill if it

◯ and write:

pill				_ _ _ _
kiss				_ _ _ _
sip				_ _ _ _
in				_ _ _
Tim				_ _ _ _
hit				_ _ _
fix				_ _ _ _

28

Match and write:

Miss

FISH
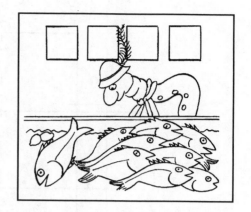

IN

bill

HILL

MIX

Write:

30

Fill in the blanks:

sick   pin   sit

zip   lid   fix   kick

The baby can ___ up.

Jim will ___ up his jacket.

Kim has to ___ the bike.

Tim plays ___ ball.

Rick has a ___ in his cap.

Jill put a ___ on the pot.

Sid feels ___ .

Who slid down the hill?

_____ _____ _____ did.

Write:

pig

Kim

hip

bib

rib

Jill

pin

lid

lip

Mick

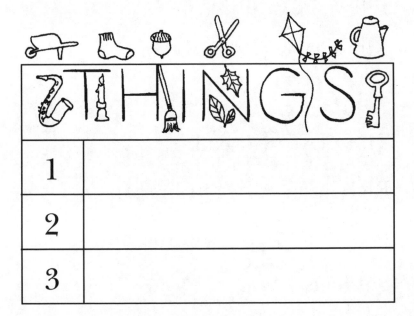

	BODY PARTS
1	
2	
3	

	THINGS
1	
2	
3	

	PEOPLE
1	
2	
3	

X the one that does not belong:

Rick
Jim
Bill
zip

pill
Mick
mitt
bib

hid
pig
did
lit

Jill
Kim
Lil
it

Think about the **sounds**. Complete the pattern.

fill	fix	fib	_____		zip
pill	pin	pit	_____		pig
wick	kick	lick	_____		sick
					bib
rip	nip	lip	_____		fin

Think about the **meanings**. Complete the pattern.

			_____		mitt
			_____		hill
			_____		lip
					pig
			_____		Jim

Where do these belong?
* = bonus words!!

pins	lid
Rick	Liz
bib	* dish
Tim	* Missy

CABINET

1. _____

2. _____

3. _____

4. _____

SCHOOL BUS

1. _____

2. _____

3. _____

4. _____

35

Here is a page from a book I like.
Circle all the **short-i** words.

He slid down the hill and missed
the tree by an inch.

Look in a book **you** like. Find a word with **short-i** in it. Put it in a sentence. Then draw a picture to go with your sentence.

Write:

Sid will fix
the _____.

Lil will fix the dish
with the _____.

Tim will fix
the _____.

Mick   fix   hill   Jill   mitt   pin

_____ will fix
the crib.

Liz will _____
the sink.

_____ will fix
the grill.

What will *you* fix?

I will fix the   _____

_____

Cut on solid lines and fold on dotted lines. Put together to form booklet. Staple and color.

big smile!

8

BIG

Big bat,

1

big miss,

6

big mitts,

3

big ball,

2

big hit . . .

7

big kids,

4

big swing,

5

FOLD

FOLD

I wish

Hi! I'm the Ugly Duckling. I look for **short-u** clues.

Here are some . . .

up **u**s

under **u**mbrella

Let's look for some more **ŭ** clues . . .

Write:

rug	mug	bug
	_ _ _ _ _ _
	_ _ _ _ _ _
	_ _ _ _ _ _

sun	bun	run
	_ _ _ _ _ _
	_ _ _ _ _ _
	_ _ _ _ _ _

up	pup	cup
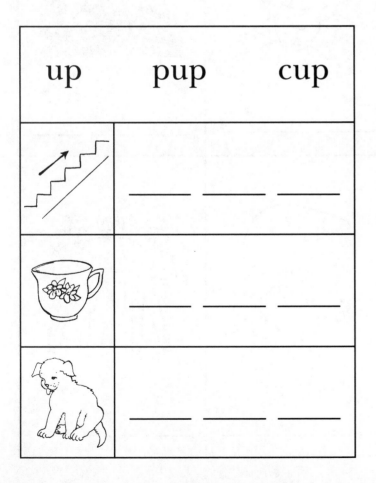	_ _ _ _ _ _
	_ _ _ _ _ _
	_ _ _ _ _ _

sub	cub	tub
	_ _ _ _ _ _
	_ _ _ _ _ _
	_ _ _ _ _ _

43

Write:

jug			
tug			
hug	_____	_____	_____

bud			
mud			
Judd	_____	_____	_____

us			
bus			
Gus	_____	_____	_____

44

Write:

	＿ ＿ ＿ ＿ ＿	cut
	＿ ＿ ＿ ＿	cuff
	＿ ＿ ＿ ＿	cub

	＿ ＿ ＿	buzz
	＿ ＿ ＿	bud
	＿ ＿ ＿ ＿ ＿	bug

	＿ ＿ ＿ ＿ ＿	gull
	＿ ＿ ＿ ＿	gum
	＿ ＿ ＿ ＿	Gus

45

◯ and write:

d	g	u	x	m	t

c	e	h	u	p	k

g	b	v	u	s	n

c	r	s	u	i	g

d	m	u	b	ll	ck

c	j	u	r	ff	ck

f	t	z	u	b	l

n	b	u	w	t	p

46

bun mud bud dug	tuck cut cup rut	us fuss up sun
tub rug gut tug	lug gull Gus dull	but mutt mug tuck
pup hut us up	bun bus fun nut	mug gum hug hum
bus sub sun rub	Buff fuzz cuff cub	bug jug bud dug
luck duck dull cup	bun nut rug run	mud mutt bud hum

cub				_ _ _
fun				_ _ _
pup				_ _ _
hum				_ _ _
cut				_ _ _
mug				_ _ _
buzz				_ _ _ _

Match and write:

UP

CUP

BUS

rugs

CUT

GUM

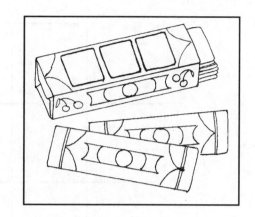

on the dotted line

Name
School

Write:

Fill in the blanks:

rug   hug   mud

sun   duck   cut   run

Muffy gave the puppy a 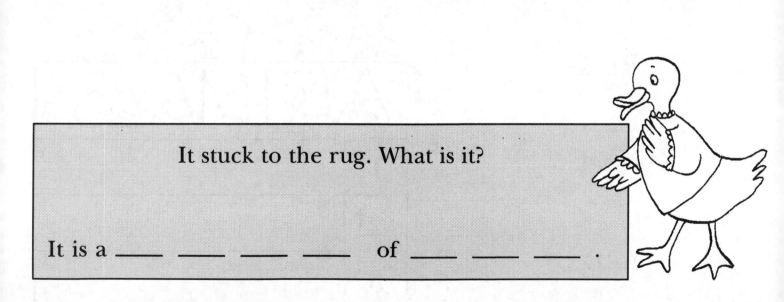 .   ___ ___

Russ 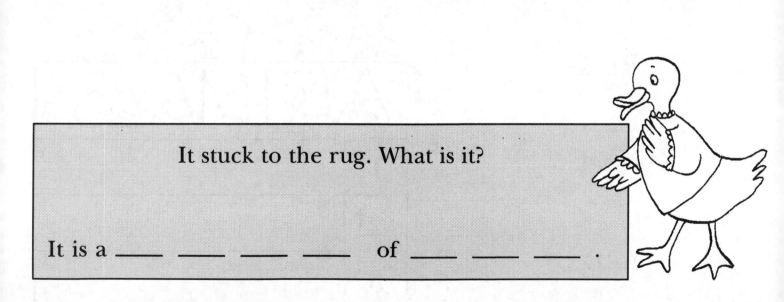 his leg.   ___ ___

The kids 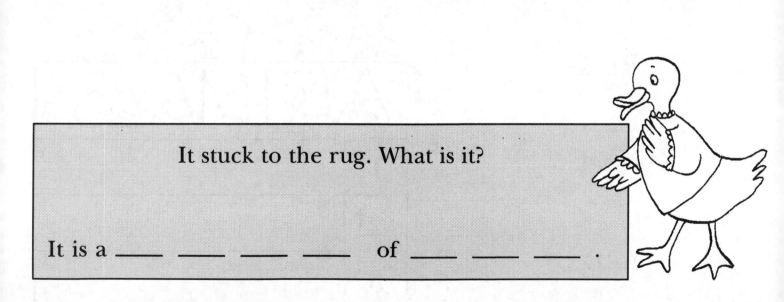 to the bus.   ___ ___ ___

The toy 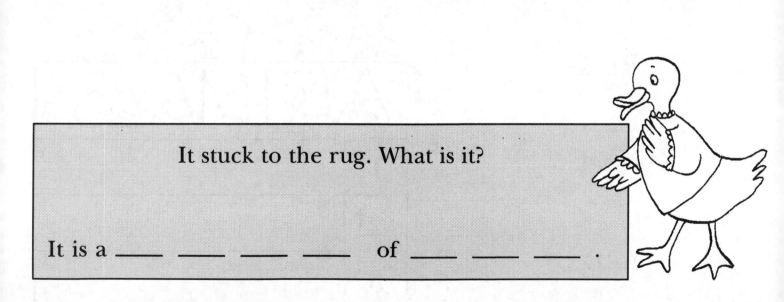 is in the tub.   ___ ___ ___

The 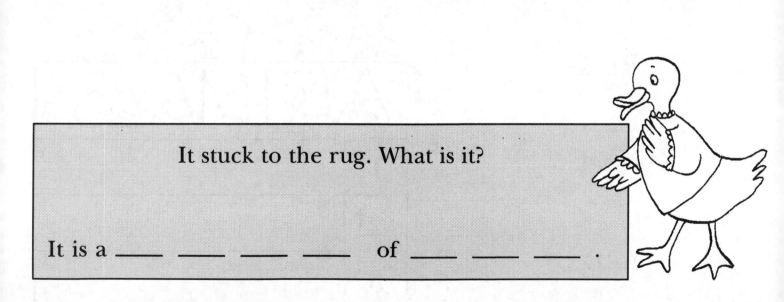 is fuzzy.   ___ ___

The 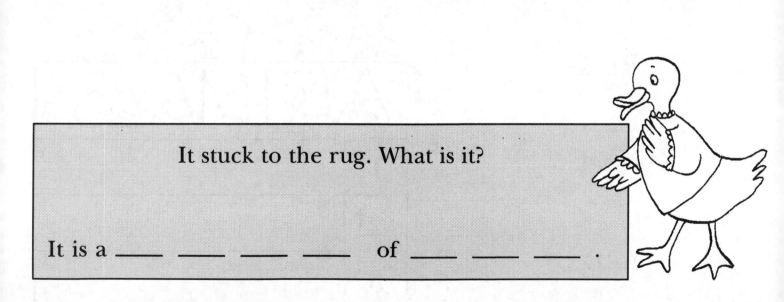 is up.   ___ ___ ___

The truck got stuck in the 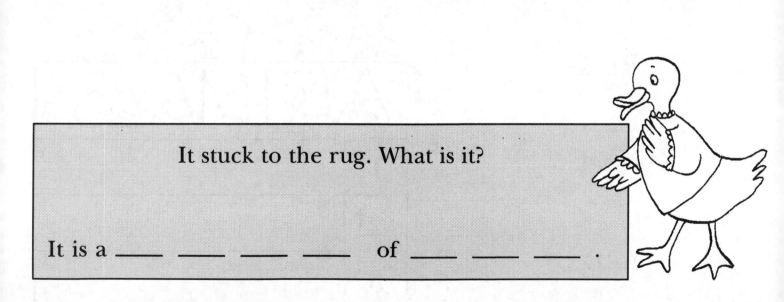 .   ___ ___

It stuck to the rug. What is it?

It is a ___ ___ ___ ___ of ___ ___ ___ .

51

Write:

pup

up

rug

Bud

cub

Judd

cup

Russ

duck

mug

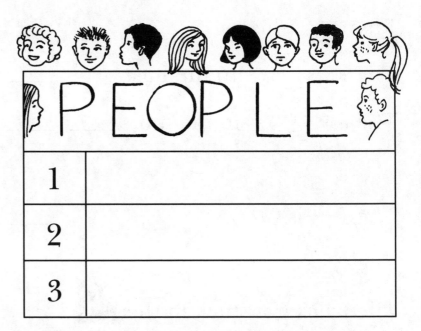

THINGS	
1	
2	
3	

PEOPLE	
1	
2	
3	

ANIMALS	
1	
2	
3	

X the one that does not belong:

hug

hum

Judd

run

Gus

cut

Russ

Bud

sun

pup

cub

duck

mug

cup

jug

up

Think about the **sounds**. Complete the **pattern**.

bug	but	bun	_____	rug
cup	cuff	cut	_____	cub
tug	mug	hug	_____	bud
				sun
bun	fun	run	_____	pup

Think about the **meanings**. Complete the pattern.

			_____	fun
			_____	bus
			_____	cuff
				cub
			_____	cup

54

Where do these belong?
* = bonus word!

buns	mug
bugs	mud
sun	buds
cup	* mustard

KITCHEN SHELF

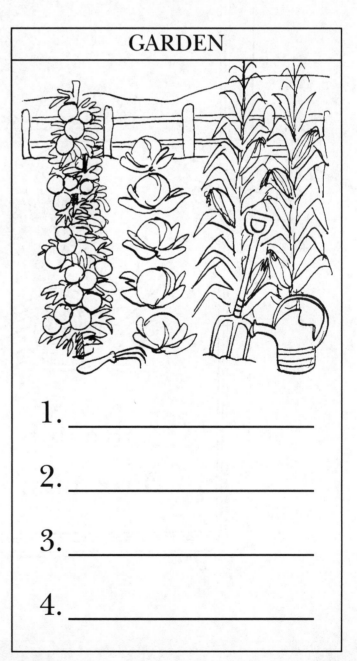

1. _____

2. _____

3. _____

4. _____

GARDEN

1. _____

2. _____

3. _____

4. _____

56

Find a **short-u** word in a book **you** like. Put it in a sentence. Draw a picture to go with your sentence.

Write:

Russ had fun in the _____.

Judd had fun in the _____.

Gus had fun in the _____.

sun   fun   Bud   tub   mud   bus

Muffy had fun in the _____.

Rusty had _____ in the puddle.

_____ had fun in the bucket.

Where did you have fun?

I had fun --

58

us!

8

FOLD

1

fuzzy bugs,

6

FOLD

fuzzy kittens,

3

59

Fuzzy pups,

2

fuzzy . . .

7

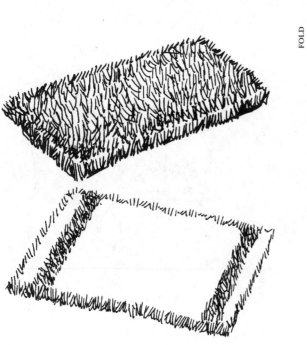

fuzzy rugs,

4

fuzzy mittens,

5

Hi! I'm Ella the Elephant. I look for **short-e** clues.

Here are some . . .

exit

end

egg

elf

Let's look for some more ĕ clues . . .

Write:

jet net pet	
	_ _ _
	_ _ _
	_ _ _

bell fell sell	
	_ _ _ _
	_ _ _ _
	_ _ _ _

hen men pen	
	_ _ _
	_ _ _
	_ _ _

leg beg egg	
	_ _ _
	_ _ _
	_ _ _

Write:

vet wet met			
deck neck peck			
bed red fed			

_ _ _

64

Write:

	___ ___ ___	Tex
	___ ___ ___ ___	ten
	___ ___ ___	tell

	___ ___ ___	web
	___ ___ ___ ___	well
	___ ___ ___	wet

	___ ___ ___	mess
	___ ___ ___	men
	___ ___ ___ ___	Meg

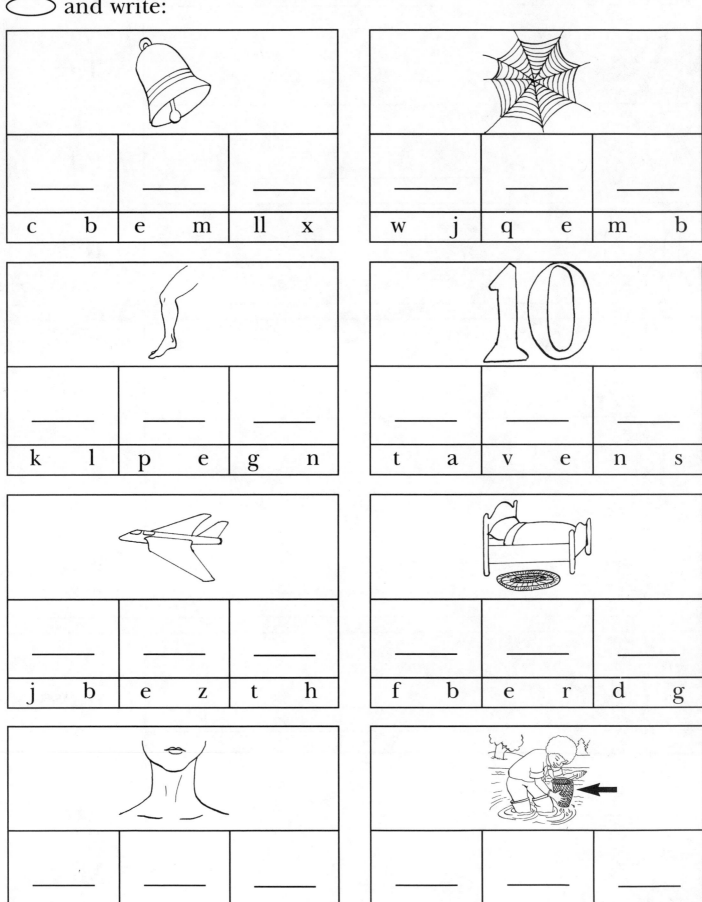

and write:

c	b	e	m	ll	x

w	j	q	e	m	b

k	l	p	e	g	n

t	a	v	e	n	s

j	b	e	z	t	h

f	b	e	r	d	g

l	n	e	t	g	ck

n	d	f	e	l	t

fell wed fed den	yell yet dell let	met yes set mess
bed Deb deck web	Ned net ten get	deck Ken peck pen
Rex Deb pep yes	hen Ben hem net	bell egg peg beg
tell fell fed led	jet jell Jeff fed	hem met hen gem
wet vet vex yet	mess let sell less	pet Peg beg get

and write:

wet				_ _ _
egg				_ _ _
mess				_ _ _ _
tell				_ _ _ _
web				_ _ _
deck				_ _ _ _
red				_ _ _

Match and write:

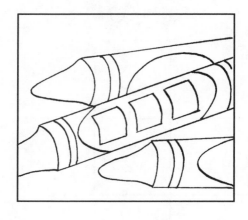

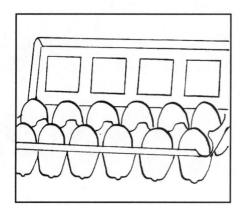

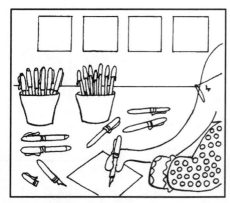

Write:

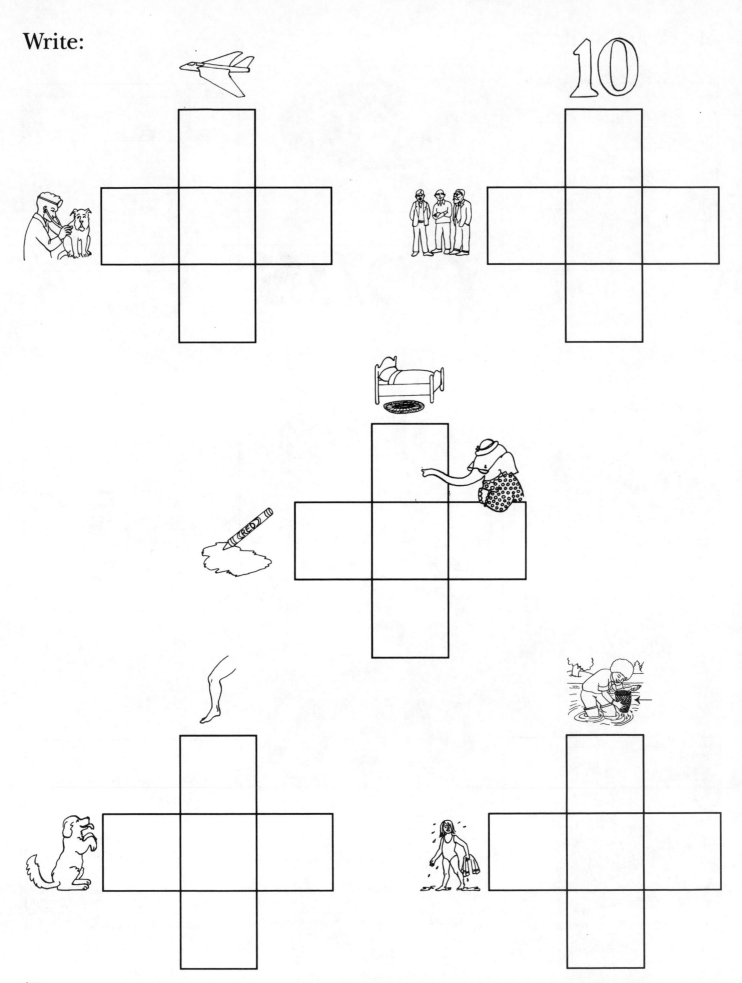

70

Fill in the blanks:

bell   men   ten

web   egg   leg   wet

The hen sat on the ⬭ .   ___ ___ | ___

The 🧑‍🤝‍🧑 are on the deck.   ___ | ___

Debby has 10 cents. | ___ ___

The hen gets 🧍 .   ___ ___

The spider spins a 🕸 .   ___ | ___

Ed cut his 🦵 . | ___ ___

Rex rang the school 🔔 .   ___ ___ | ___

Peg is sick,

but she will ___ ___ ___   ___ ___ ___ ___ .

Write:

Deb

pen

Peg

yet

Ted

bed

Jeff

Meg

bell

Ben

THINGS	
1	
2	
3	

GIRLS	
1	
2	
3	

BOYS	
1	
2	
3	

X the one that does not belong:

bell	Jeff
yes	Ken
pen	Ted
net	egg

met	Deb
led	jet
Jess	Meg
fell	Bess

Think about the **sounds**. Complete the **pattern**.

bell	bet	beg	_____	Meg
mess	men	met	_____	web
pen	Ken	ten	_____	yell
well	fell	sell	_____	bed
				hen

Think about the **meanings**. Complete the pattern.

			_____	ten
3	4	12	_____	red
BLUE	GREEN	YELLOW	_____	neck
			_____	jet
				hen

Where do these belong?
* = bonus word!

jet	* nest
pen	* desk
tent	* T.V. set
bed	bell

INSIDE

1. _____

2. _____

3. _____

4. _____

OUTSIDE

1. _____

2. _____

3. _____

4. _____

Here is a page from a book I like.
Circle all the **short-e** words.

"Help!" yelled Freddy as he
landed on the floor.

He looked up and saw the bed
next to him.

"I fell out of bed!"

Look in a book **you** like. Find a word with **short-e** in it. Put it in a sentence. Draw a picture to go with your sentence.

Write:

Jeff fell on

the _____.

Meg fell on

the _____.

Ben fell on

the _____.

egg   steps   pen   deck   jet   bed

Peg fell on

the _____.

Ken fell on

the _____.

Nell fell on

the _____.

What did you fall on?

I fell on the _____

78

School!

8

LET'S GO!

Pencils,

1

Deb,

6

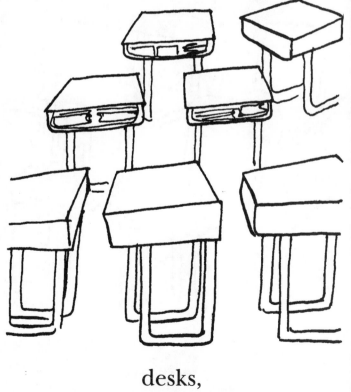

desks,

3

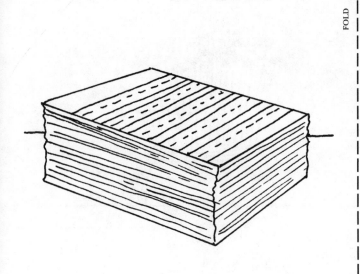

paper,

2

bell . . .

7

chairs,

4

Jeff,

5

I get scared when

when

Hi! I'm Oscar the octopus. I look for **short-o** clues.

Here are some . . .

ox   olive

octopus orange

Let's look for some more ŏ clues . . .

Write:

ox fox box	
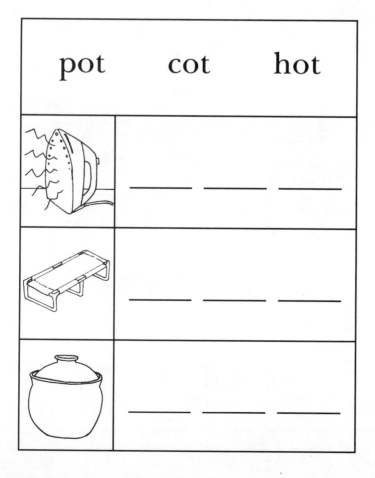	___ ___ ___
	___ ___ ___
	___ ___ ___

mop hop cop	
	___ ___ ___
	___ ___ ___
	___ ___ ___

pot cot hot	
	___ ___ ___
	___ ___ ___
	___ ___ ___

job rob Bob	
	___ ___ ___
	___ ___ ___
	___ ___ ___

Write:

dog log hog	_ _ _ _ _	_ _ _ _ _	_ _ _ _ _
dot lot pot	_ _ _ _ _	_ _ _ _ _	_ _ _ _ _
lock rock sock	_ _ _ _ _	_ _ _ _ _	_ _ _ _ _

Write:

	— — —	**Ron**
	— — —	**rock**
	— — — —	**rod**

	— — — —	**doll**
	— — — —	**Don**
	— — —	**dock**

	— — —	**log**
	— — — —	**lock**
	— — —	**lot**

85

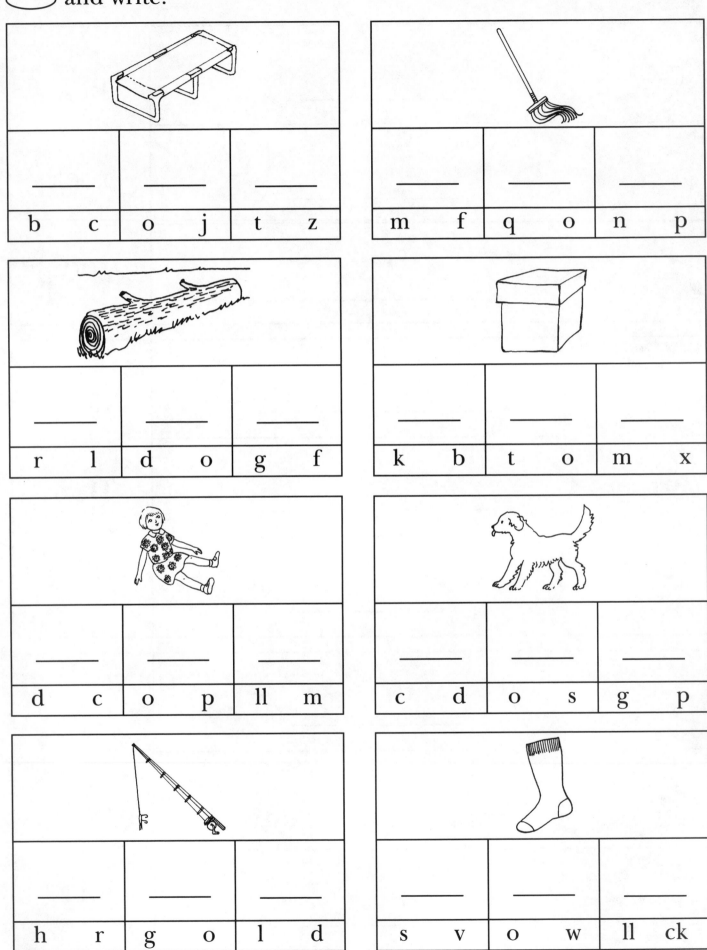

◯ and write:

b	c	o	j	t	z

m	f	q	o	n	p

r	l	d	o	g	f

k	b	t	o	m	x

d	c	o	p	ll	m

c	d	o	s	g	p

h	r	g	o	l	d

s	v	o	w	ll	ck

◯ :

hot log hog hop	jot job bog rob	doll lot dock lock
top Todd pod dot	doll lock dock dot	mop tam Mom off
top pop hop pot	fog fox hog got	got dot Todd dock
Lon doll tot lot	box fox ox on	lock log hog doll
nod Don dot on	pop pod hop mop	rot nod pod rod

and write:

rob				___ ___ ___
lock				___ ___ ___ ___
cop				___ ___ ___
Mom				___ ___ ___
Don				___ ___ ___
hot				___ ___ ___
fox				___ ___ ___

Match and write:

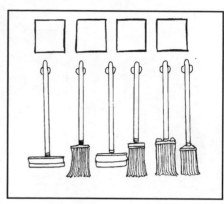

SOCKS

hot dogs

BOB

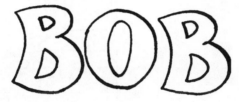
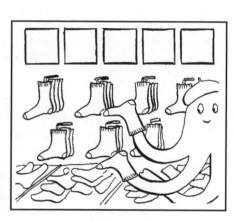

MOPS

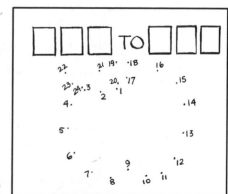

JOBS

dot·to·dot

Write:

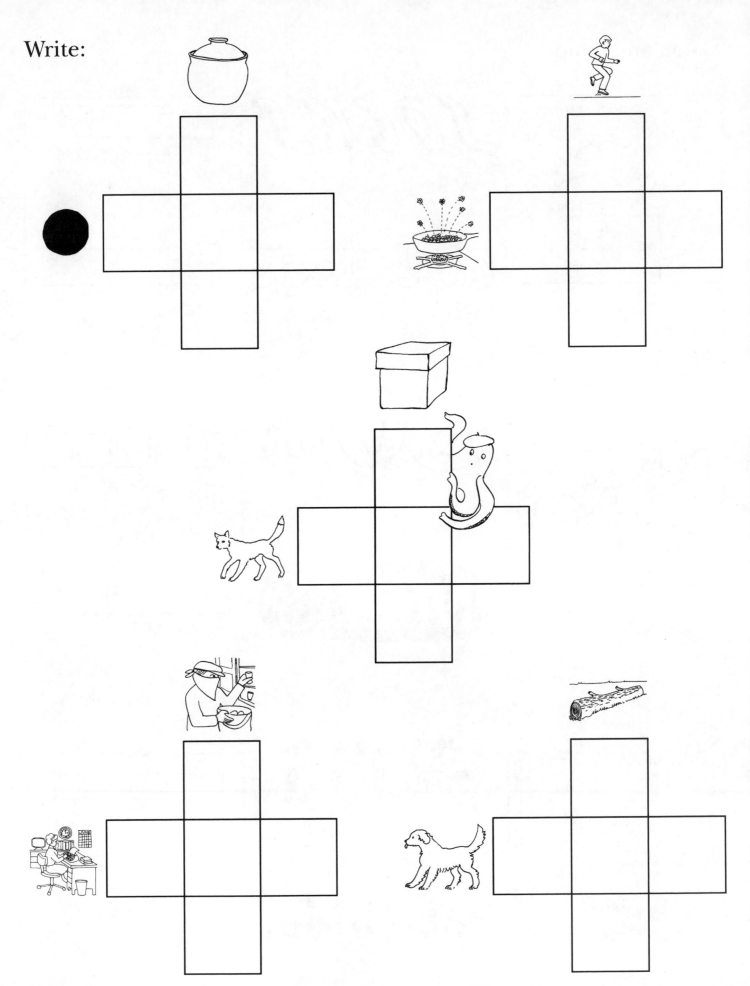

Fill in the blanks:

pot	cop	sock
rod	hop	rock

The rabbit can ____ .

The ____ is cotton.

The lobster is in the ____ .

Ron sat on top of the ____ .

The ____ got the robber.

Mom has a fishing ____ .

Don got in a car. What is it?

It is a ____ ____ ____   ____ ____ ____ .

Write:

ox

Mom

cot

pot

dog

Bob

got

cop

fox

mop

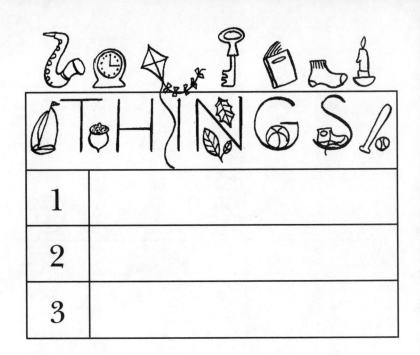

THINGS	
1	
2	
3	

PEOPLE	
1	
2	
3	

ANIMALS	
1	
2	
3	

X the one that does not belong:

mop
doll
pot
odd

hop
rock
cot
box

fox
dog
Mom
ox

Todd
hot
Don
Ron

Think about the **sounds**. Complete the **pattern**.

rob	rock	Ron	_____	mop
jot	job	jot	_____	jog
pot	cot	tot	_____	Mom
				rod
cop	hop	top	_____	hot

Think about the **meanings**. Complete the pattern.

			_____	fox
			_____	rock
				sock
			_____	Mom
			_____	mop

Where do these belong?
* = bonus word!

cot	mop
log	box
pot	rock
* pond	* frog

INSIDE

1. _____

2. _____

3. _____

4. _____

OUTSIDE

1. _____

2. _____

3. _____

4. _____

Here is a page from a book I like.
Circle all the **short-o** words.

Bobby got a can of corn.
Pop-pop-poppity-pop.
He put the corn into a pot.
Pop-pop-poppity-pop.
Soon the corn began to pop.
Pop-pop-poppity-pop.

The corn popped up and hit the top.
Pop-pop-poppity-pop.
After a while the popping stopped.
Pop-pop-poppity-pop.
Then Bobby ate the popcorn hot.
Crunch-crunch-crunchity-crunch!

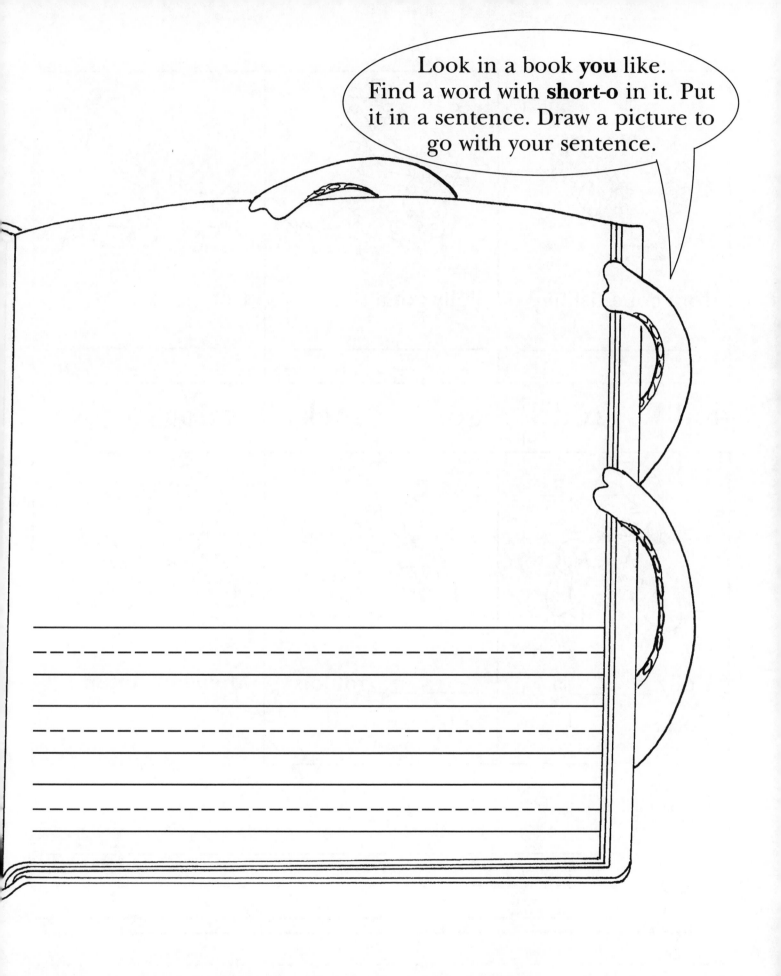

Look in a book **you** like.
Find a word with **short-o** in it. Put
it in a sentence. Draw a picture to
go with your sentence.

Write:

Tom got a fishing

_____.

Polly got a

_____.

Don got a

_____.

doll   rod   got   socks   dog   Rob

Holly _____ a
clock.

_____ got lots
of blocks.

Mom got cotton

_____.

What did *you* get?

I got   _____

_____

98

FOLD

THE BOX

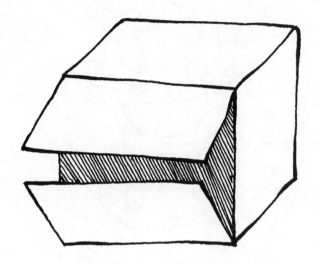

1

in the box.

8

FOLD

by the box,

6

off the box,

3

On the box,

through the box,

over the box,

under the box,

My hobby
is collecting rocks.
What is your hobby?

My hobby is

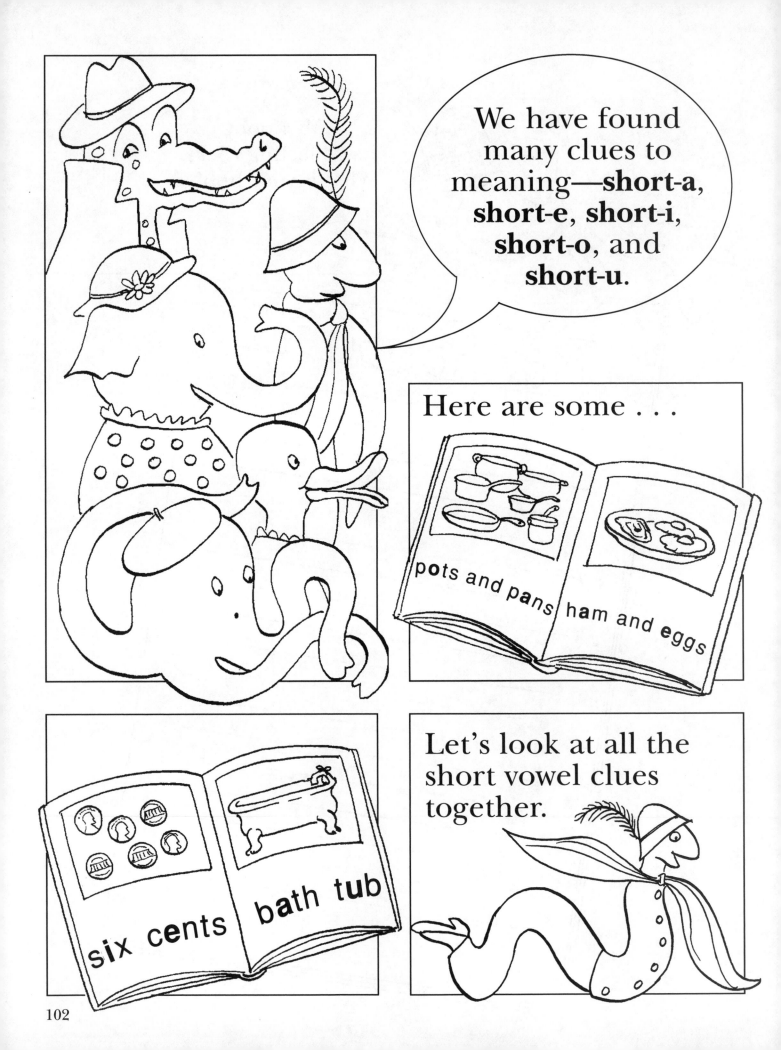

We have found many clues to meaning—**short-a**, **short-e**, **short-i**, **short-o**, and **short-u**.

Here are some . . .

pots and pans | ham and eggs

six cents | bath tub

Let's look at all the short vowel clues together.

Write:

bat mat hat	
	___ ___ ___
	___ ___ ___
	___ ___ ___

pot cot dot	
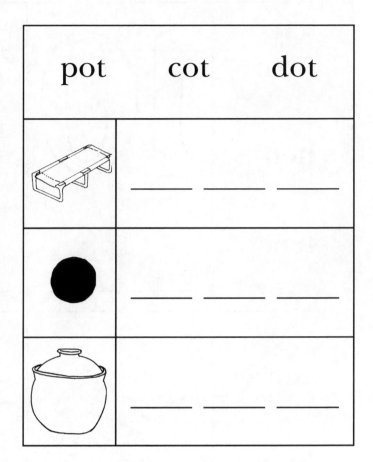	___ ___ ___
	___ ___ ___
	___ ___ ___

sit hit bit	
	___ ___ ___
	___ ___ ___
	___ ___ ___

pet wet jet	
	___ ___ ___
	___ ___ ___
	___ ___ ___

Write:

men hen ten			
sun bun run			
in fin win			

104

Write:

	— — —	cup
	— — —	cop
	— — —	cap

	— — — —	sick
	— — — —	sack
	— — — —	sock

	— — —	pin
	— — —	pen
	— — —	pan

○ and write:

f	r	o	a	ck	ll

j	f	o	e	m	t

b	z	u	i	p	g

d	g	e	a	v	s

h	b	o	e	x	t

l	t	u	i	b	n

r	l	u	e	g	p

j	h	i	a	ll	ck

lip lap pill tip	ten Ned ← not net	sock sick sack cots
bass Bess sub bus	nap pen pin pan	cub buck cup cob
sill sell yell lass	**wax** wicks mix **six**	gem jam Jim ham
red rid rod Rex	pot tip top tap	fat fan fun fin
had hit hot hut	as is us up	lot got gull log

◯ and write:

fan				_ _ _
pot				_ _ _
bug				_ _ _
him				_ _ _
net				_ _ _
ox				_ _
cap				_ _ _

Match and write:

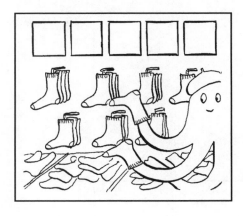

ham

SOCKS

IN

Pets

BUS

POTS

Write:

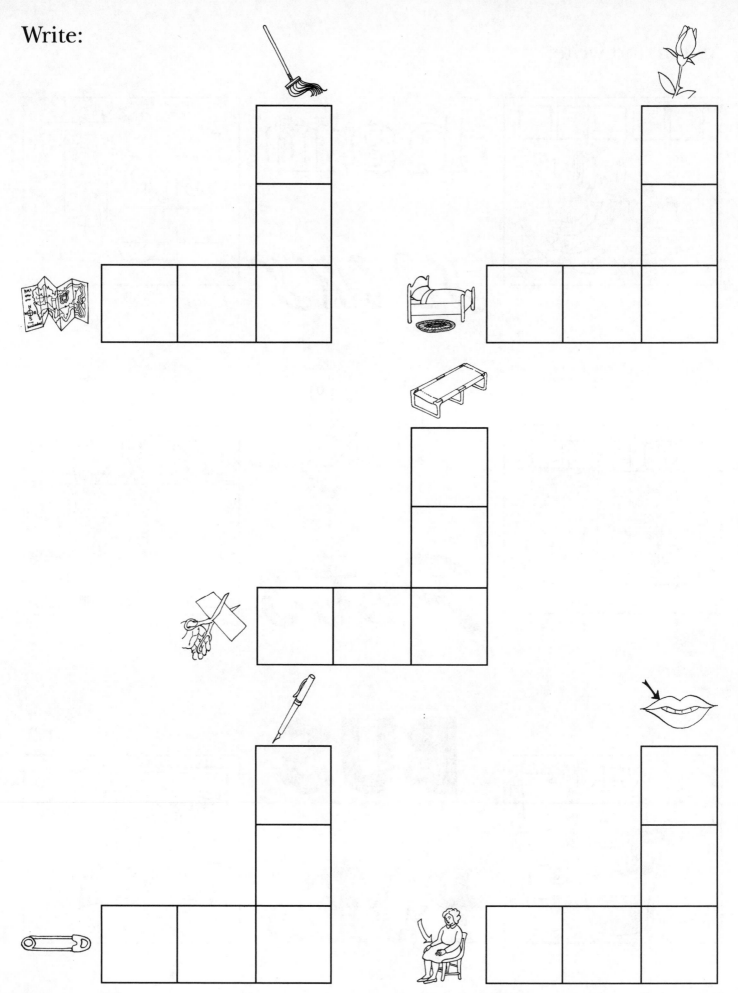

Fill in the blanks:

six	log	cup	hat
rag	sun	bed	

Mom tucked Pat into 🛏 . ___ ___ ___

The dog had 6 pups. ___ ___ ___

Rob fell off the 🪵 . ___ ___ ___

Kim has on a sun 👒 . ___ ___ ___

Fill the ☕ with milk. ___ ___ ___

Gus got the 🧽 wet. ___ ___ ___

It is hot in the ☀ . ___ ___ ___

What did the kids get from Mom?

They got ___ ___ ___   ___ ___ ___ ___ ___ .

Write:

duck

vet

rib

jacks

pig

doll

leg

top

back

fox

run

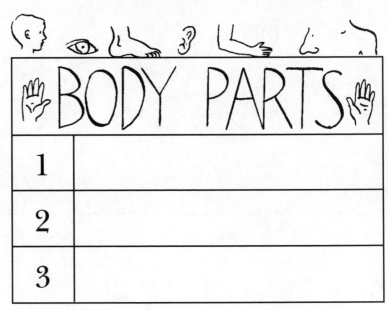

1	
2	
3	

1	
2	
3	

1	
2	
3	

X the one that does not belong:

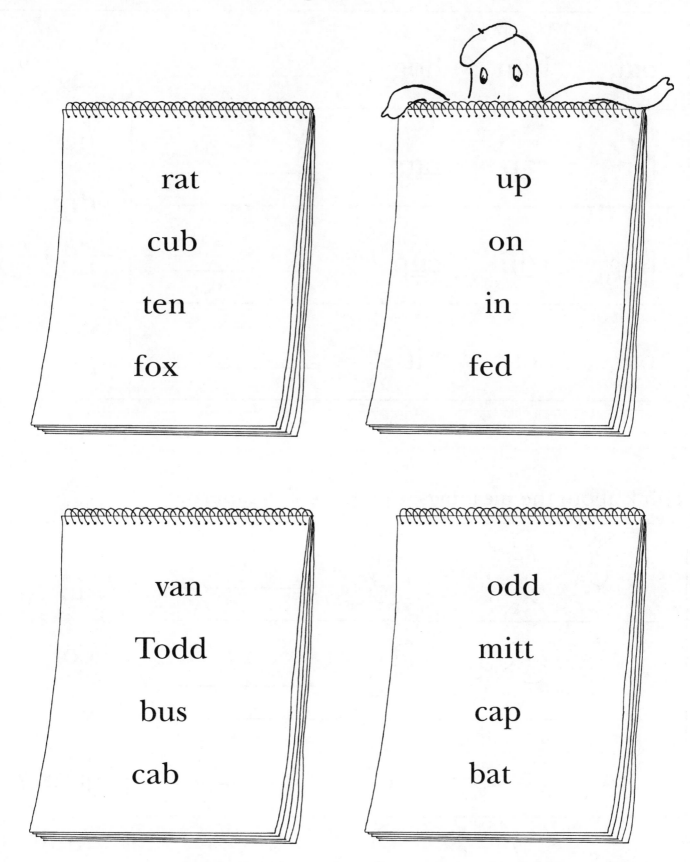

rat

cub

ten

fox

up

on

in

fed

van

Todd

bus

cab

odd

mitt

cap

bat

Think about the **sounds**. Complete the **pattern**.

hat	him	hog	_____	sag
fat	cap	ram	_____	hen
hug	run	cup	_____	dip
pat	set	bit	_____	bud
				cot

Think about the **meanings**. Complete the pattern.

			_____	lip
			_____	cot
			_____	vet
			_____	jam
				mug

Where do these belong?
* = bonus word!

top	jacks
ham	jam
doll	* puppet
eggs	* milk

TOY CHEST

1. _____

2. _____

3. _____

4. _____

REFRIGERATOR

1. _____

2. _____

3. _____

4. _____

Here is a page from a book I like.
Circle all the words with short vowels.

Jack and Jill
went up the hill
to fetch a pail of water.

Jack fell down
and broke his crown,
and Jill came tumbling after.

Find a short-vowel word in a book **you** like. Put it in a sentence. Then draw a picture to go with your sentence.

Write:

Rick _____ the back steps.

Jan _____ up the mess.

Bob _____ the table.

picks   Russ   fills   van   mops   sets

Peg waxes the _____.

_____ scrubs the pots.

Dan _____ the trash can.

What job do you do?

I _____

118

$\bigcirc$ the word.

l	c	s
h	o	t
p	f	d

n	m	v
g	a	j
t	p	s

r	e	d
u	w	o
k	i	b

c	p	r
m	o	m
q	n	e

b	k	v
f	u	j
r	l	s

Help Kim write a letter back to Debby.
Use the words in the box.

six	dog	run	Debby	naps

Sept. 15

Dear _____

    I have a pet. It is a _____. It _____ on my bed.

    I am _____ years old. I can _____ fast.

      Please write back!
      Your pen pal,
        Kim

TIME FOR . . .

1

. . . breakfast!

8

Jill and Tom,

6

toast and jam,

3

Eggs and ham,

2

Dad and Mom,

7

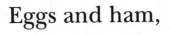

milk and juice,

4

muf•fins, too.

5